Jane Smisor Bastien · Lisa Bastien · Lori Bastien

BASTIENS'
COLLAGE
OF SOLOS

Bastiens' Collage of Solos, Book 2, is designed to captivate the interest and imagination of beginning students with the three distinctive styles of Jane, Lisa, and Lori Bastien. These solos will add excitement to the elementary repertoire for all beginning students!

Contents

✓ *

*To reinforce the feeling of achievement, the teacher or student may put a ✓ when the page has been mastered.

ISBN 0-8497-9623-7

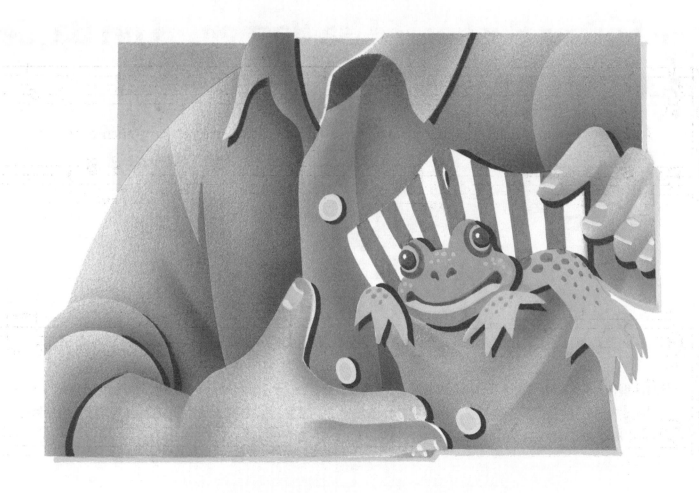

Frog in My Pocket

Lisa Bastien

Allegretto

mf I was run-ning down the lane, pre-tend-ing to be a plane. When I

saw a nice big frog, he jumped from be-neath a log.

p I asked him if he want-ed to play. He said, "Sure, it is such a nice day!

mf Leap Frog's best it's my fav-o-rite game." *f* I like it too. We think the same. Now the

sun has near-ly set. I'd like you to be my pet. In my pock-et you could

stay. We'd play each and ev'-ry day. We'd play each and ev'-ry day. Yeah!

The Magic Clown

Jane Smisor Bastien

Allegro con spirito

mf Oh, the Mag-ic Clown, he's lots of fun. He can fool most an-y-one. When he

Both hands play one octave higher on repeat

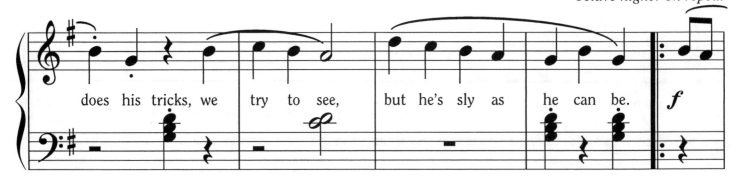

does his tricks, we try to see, but he's sly as he can be. *f*

Just Imagine

Lori Bastien

Jumbo Jet

Jane Smisor Bastien

Moderato

mf Oh, a - way we go in a jum - bo jet. We will have a lot of fun. Ei - ther

bring your skis or your rac - quet, please. We may use both or just one.

f Now is our va - ca - tion and we could - n't wait to go. We'll see all our re - la - tives and

I Love to Make You Smile

Lori Bastien

Choc - 'lates I would send. Toys and games I'd lend.

I'd do al - most an - y -thing for you, my friend!

If you're lone - ly, down and out, all you have to do is shout.

Call me up, I'd trav - el miles. I love to make you smile!

My Treasure Chest

Jane Smisor Bastien

Boardwalk Arcade

Lisa Bastien

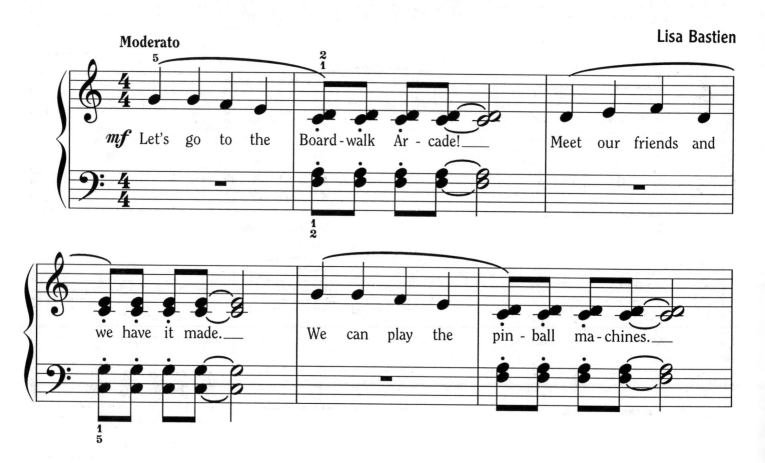

Moderato

mf Let's go to the Board-walk Ar-cade!___ Meet our friends and

we have it made.___ We can play the pin-ball ma-chines.___

Saturday Morning Boogie

Lori Bastien

I am the Captain

Lisa Bastien

In a Far Off Land

Jane Smisor Bastien

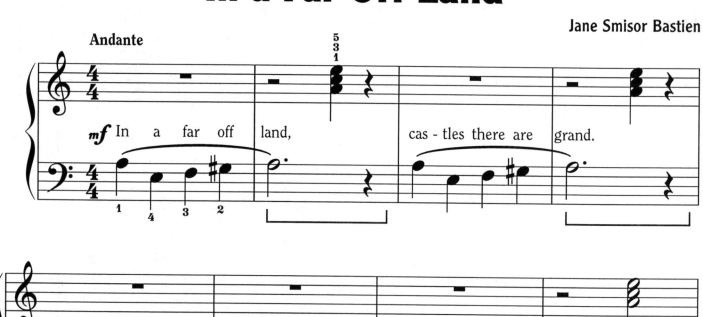

In a far off land, cas - tles there are grand.

Peo - ple just like you and me go to look and see.

Ice Skating at Rockefeller Center

Lori Bastien

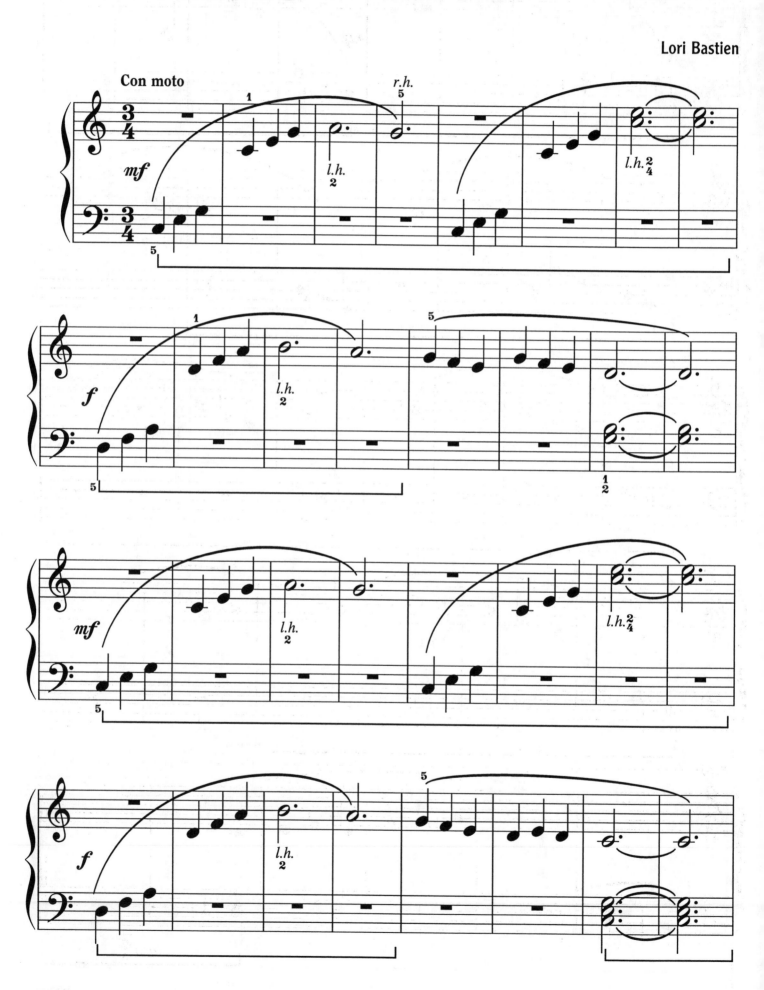

About the Composers

Jane Smisor Bastien is the former director of the Preparatory Department of Music at Tulane University, where she had an extensive background in developing teaching materials for children. Jane graduated Phi Beta Kappa from Barnard College and received her Master of Arts degree from Teachers College, Columbia University. Jane has authored and coauthored more than 300 books with her husband James and with their daughters, Lisa Bastien Hanss and Lori Bastien Vickers. Jane created **The Very Young Pianist Library** and **Bastiens' Invitation to Music**, methods written expressly for very young students. She and her husband James Bastien created the **Bastien Piano Library**, **Bastien Piano Basics**, and **Bastien Older Beginner Library**, methods for beginners of all ages. Jane and her husband James live in La Jolla, California.

Lisa Bastien began piano lessons at the age of 4, studying with her mother at the Preparatory Department of Tulane University in New Orleans. She received her Bachelor of Music in Piano Performance from Drake University and her Master's Degree in Piano Pedagogy from Arizona State University. After receiving her Master's Degree, Lisa moved to New Orleans and taught in the Preparatory Department at Loyola University. Lisa Bastien, her husband Basil Hanss, and their daughter Katie reside in New York City where Lisa continues to teach private and group lessons and compose music for her students. Lisa enjoys writing fun, motivational music for all ages. To encourage learning and reinforce musical concepts, Lisa developed ideas for **Wipe-Off Books**, **Dot · to · Dot Notespeller** and **Dot · to · Dot Delight**.

Lori Bastien began lessons at the age of 4, also studying with her mother. After attending the University of Redlands, Lori transferred to Rice University where she received her Bachelor of Music degree. She teaches both group and private lessons and is very active in national and local music teacher organizations. Lori, who has been a piano teacher since her teen years, writes music that her students find fun to play. She coauthored **Bastiens' Invitation to Music** and **A Debut For You Books 1-4** with her mother Jane Smisor Bastien and her sister Lisa Bastien. Lori Bastien, her husband Eric Vickers, and their daughter Abby live in La Jolla, California.